C000022945

The BUILDING STONES of DEVON

Prepared by Mr A. W. Gale
and members of the Geological Section
of the Association,
with advice from Dr R. C. Scrivener

Line drawings by Mrs. P. Thorman

THE DEVONSHIRE ASSOCIATION
for the Advancement of Science,
Literature and the Arts

First published in 1992
by The Devonshire Association

Typeset in 11 point Palatino

Design and typesetting by
Ex Libris Press, Bradford on Avon

Printed by Shires Press, Trowbridge, Wiltshire

© Text The Devonshire Association
© Colour plates A. W. Gale

ISBN 0 85214 051 7

This booklet is dedicated to the memory of Dr Brendan Moore. Both as President and Chairman of Council, Dr Moore was keenly interested in the activities of all seventeen Branches and Sections of the Association. One of his particular interests was geology, and it was his suggestion that such a guide might be helpful to members within the Association and of interest beyond.

Cover: Prysten House, Plymouth – Devonian Limestone, Dartmoor Granite and Hurdwick Stone (slate).

CONTENTS

INTRODUCTION

Looking at the older buildings in Devon it is obvious that many of the structures have been influenced by the type of stone available in the immediate vicinity. Before our modern transport network was available, it made sense to use locally available materials.

There are , of course, exceptions. For instance, the Romans brought Purbeck marble from Dorset when constructing their fort in Exeter as well as their own Italian marble, and the Normans brought Caen stone for Exeter cathedral. From the eighteenth to the twentieth centuries Bath and Portland stone were extensively quarried and, being so readily available, were used in some of the buildings of Devon. However, this short guide concentrates on our county's own stones, of which there is a great variety, and the purpose of the guide is to assist in the identification of native building stones, particularly in older buildings.

In attempting to identify our building stones it is useful to have some knowledge of local geology, so each section of the guide has a sketch map of the county showing where the particular type of stone occurs. Stones differ greatly in strength and durability, a fact recognised by the Romans when constructing their fortifications around Exeter. The city has two stone types within its boundaries. The Romans chose the basaltic 'trap' rock as opposed to the sedimentary Heavitree breccia, and the fact that much of their wall still stands shows that they knew what they were about. When sedimentary rocks are used for exterior building work it is essential that the stone is laid by the mason the same way up as it occurred in the quarry, a principle which has not been followed in many cases. Collapsing walls and rotting window surrounds are frequent symptoms of this error.

The bulk of Devon's existing stone buildings are truly

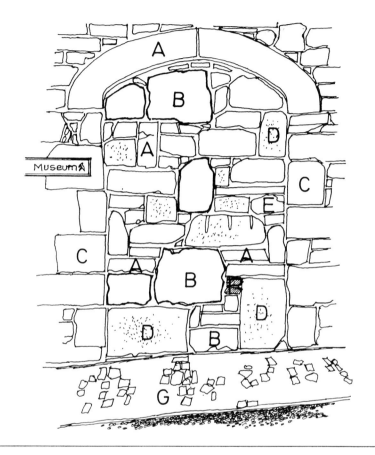

Wall in Palace Gate, Exeter

Key: A   Beer Stone
       B   Heavitree breccia
       C   Vesicular 'Trap'
       D   Granite
       E   Quartz
       F   Sandstone
       G   Quartzite pebbles from River Exe (pavement)

vernacular, built by the people using local materials wisely in the best way they could. Stones were selected not because they were the best for the job but because they were available – from a local quarry or a pit in a field, granite from the open moor or ready dressed stone recycled from a dissolved monastery or some other dilapidated building. It is this mixture of stones which makes their identification an interesting challenge.

It can, at times, be quite an interesting exercise to look at an old wall, trying to fathom out the various stones used. The example given in the illustration is part of a wall in Palace Gate, between South Street and the cathedral in Exeter. One gains the impression that new building as well as subsequent repairs were sometimes carried out using job lots of odds and ends from various convenient sources.

It is quite common for more than one stone to be used in the same building (*see* drawing on previous page). The reasons vary in each case but include making use of the different strengths of stones, being guided by differential costs and wishing to vary colour and texture in a building. The Prysten House illustrates that point, and also that stone could be transported some distance from its source on occasions (*see* drawing opposite).

At the end of each section mention is made of typical buildings where the stone being described can be seen in use, and also quarries where the stone can be seen 'in the raw'. All quarries are dangerous, and those no longer worked particularly so. Before visiting a working quarry, or an old quarry on private land, it is advisable to check whether you would be welcome. Health and Safety at Work regulations may preclude entry to a quarry, and there may also be insurance difficulties.

Although strictly speaking not a stone, there is also a section on cob walls, a traditional Devon building material. Devon has a variety of stone types, and as variety is the spice of life we hope that this guide will help you to have plenty of that.

The Prysten House, Finewell Street, Plymouth built by Thomas Yogge, merchant, in 1498

Walls: Devonian Limestone
Door and Window Surrounds: Dartmoor Granite
Dark Stones in Walls: Hurdwick Stone

1 LIMESTONES

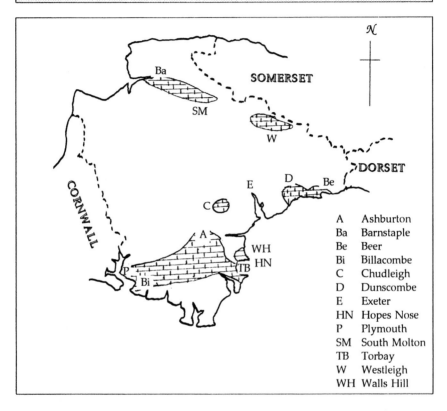

A   Ashburton
Ba   Barnstaple
Be   Beer
Bi   Billacombe
C   Chudleigh
D   Dunscombe
E   Exeter
HN   Hopes Nose
P   Plymouth
SM   South Molton
TB   Torbay
W   Westleigh
WH   Walls Hill

Limestone consists mainly of calcium and magnesium carbonate, and may contain impurities which give it distinctive colourings. Most of Devon's limestones are light to dark grey, although pink and buff staining (due mainly to iron minerals) provides local variations. The Devonian and Carboniferous limestones are far harder, and more durable, than the Cretaceous limestones. Some limestones are described, particularly by the stone polishing trade, as marbles, but true marble is actually a limestone which has been melted in the Earth's crust. On cooling it has formed a fine crystal structure – metamorphosed – and the former bedding and fossils of the limestone have disappeared.

Devonian limestones occur from Plymouth to Tor Bay, Newton Abbot and Chudleigh, and were formed from the skeletons of plants and animals, cemented together with calcium carbonate. Great thicknesses of limestone were created in which the fossil remains of the corals, bivalves etc, can be clearly distinguished. These limestones have been extensively quarried for building purposes because of their local availability and durability. Some of these stones were also cut and polished as marble – e.g. Ashburton 'marble' – but they soon lose their attractiveness when exposed to our modern atmosphere.

Quarries: Devonian limestones are currently quarried in Plymouth at Moorcroft Quarry, Billacombe (English China Clays), and Plymstock (Blue Circle); at Linhay Quarry, Ashburton (Glendinning's); Stoneycombe Quarry, Kingskerswell, (English China Clays); Yalberton Quarry, Paignton, (ARC); and Lummaton Quarry, Torquay, (ARC). Disused quarries which might possibly be visited are at Walls Hill and Hope's Nose, Torquay; and Palace Quarry, Chudleigh.

Carboniferous limestones contain similar fossil remains to the Devonian stone. They are normally of a mid-grey colour, with occasional pink colourations, and often have bands of the black mineral chert, which is similar to flint. The presence of the chert imparts a hardness to the stone, which consequently causes it to be very durable.

Carboniferous limestone is quarried near Bampton at Kersdown Quarry (Scotts [Bampton] Ltd.,) & Westleigh Quarry (English China Clays); at Fenacre Quarry near Burlescombe

(Tarmac); and at Blackaller Quarry near Drewsteignton, (Devon Quarry & Tarpaving Ltd.,), and was formerly quarried in the Barnstaple and South Molton areas of north Devon

Cretaceous limestones are distinguished by their pale beige colour, and are not as durable as the preceding limestones. They are formed mainly from fragments of shelly fossils, so that the stone has a generally gritty texture. The Beer stone and Salcombe Regis stone were much used for decorative work on churches and stately homes, as well as for the main structure of the buildings. The freshly quarried stone is soft in texture and easily worked, but it soon hardens on exposure to the air. Unfortunately our modern climate wreaks havoc on outdoor carved limestone of this age – witness the extensive repair work carried out on Exeter Cathedral.

Cretaceous limestones are worked in East Devon at Beer Quarry (ARC), and Uplyme Quarry (Glendinning Group). The old quarrying caves at Beer are well worth a visit. The Dunscombe quarry, on a private caravan site, was worked recently to obtain stone for replacements on Exeter Cathedral.

TYPICAL BUILDINGS
Devonian limestones: The Guildhall and the Citadel in Plymouth; the Royal Naval Dockyard buildings in Devonport; the Town Hall and the Old Hospital, Higher Union Street, Torquay; the Clock Tower, Courtenay Street, Newton Abbot; and the old Royal Infirmary, Southernhay, Exeter.
Carboniferous limestones: Boundary walls by the County Hall; opposite the School for the Deaf, Topsham Road; and the Chuch of the Blessed Sacrament, South Street, all in Exeter.
Cretaceous limestones: Exeter Cathedral, and many churches in south east Devon.

2 SANDSTONES

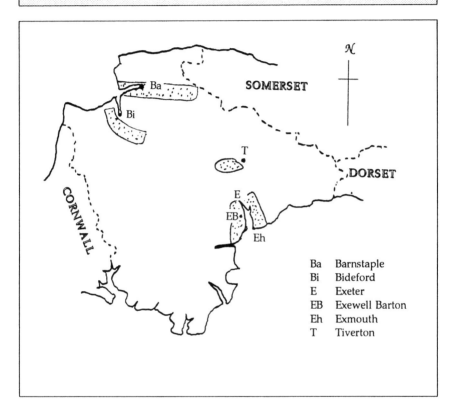

Sandstone, as its name implies, consists mainly of sand particles, which have been cemented together, to form rock. Usually the sand grains can be seen to be rounded when examined with a hand lens but angular fragments are also commonly present. The sand grains are normally quartz fragments, but other minerals, such as micas and feldspars, may be present. The cementing mineral is often silica or calcium carbonate but sometimes iron oxides stick the grains together. The properties of the cementing mineral determine the durability of the sandstone, as sand on its own soon crumbles when dry.

As sandstone is a sedimentary rock it often displays quite obvious 'bedding', and quite frequently the variations which occurred during the sedimentation processes are revealed by noticeable changes in the sizes of the sand grains. Geologists call a sandstone which is cemented together with silica an orthoquartzite, and quartzites are among the most resistant rocks known.

Some of the north Devon sandstones are so fine grained that one could well be forgiven for thinking that they are tough limestones but use of the hand lens to look for the sand grains may help. The Devonian sandstones of north Devon have been partially metamorphosed, and it is often difficult to distinguish the sand grains. Should you, by any chance, have a bottle of dilute hydrochloric acid with you, a drop or two of this on the stone would help to resolve the matter, as limestone fizzes quite delightfully when the acid is applied. Remember, however, that what the acid can do to a rock it can more easily do to you!

Beware of thinking that the presence of rounded grains means that the rock is necessarily sandstone. Some limestones are oolitic, that is they consist of lime particles which have formed around a nucleus in shallow waters, the particles looking like fish roes. Have a look at a piece of Bath stone with a hand lens to 'get your eye in' on oolitic limestones. Also, nature being what it is, it is sometimes a matter for debate as to whether the minerals present make the stone a calcareous sandstone, or a sandy limestone: the major mineral usually wins.

Sandstones vary considerably in colour from pure white to beige, brown, red and even green or mauve; the trace impurities (usually iron oxides) lightly coating each sand grain have an effect far greater than their volume.

The rusty brown faces of some sandstones, particularly those of north Devon, can easily be mistaken for the similarly coloured Mill Hill slates of the Tavistock area. A scratch with a pen knife blade will reveal which is which. The sandstone will leave abrasions on the knife blade, whereas the metal will gouge the face of the slate.

Quarries: Devonian sandstone quarries now working are Plaistow and Bray Valley Quarries (A. Nott & Sons Ltd.), and Barton Wood Quarry (Devon County Council), both near Barnstaple. Carboniferous sandstone is worked near Bideford at Bableigh Wood (D. E. Chance Ltd.); at Beam Quarry, Great Torrington, (Torrington Stone Ltd.); Venn Quarry (English China Clays) and Hearson Quarry (Hearson Quarry [Swimbridge] Ltd), both near Barnstaple; Hayne Quarry (R. W. T. Edworthy) and Tuckingmill Quarry (Aubrey Sanders), both at Bow; and Knowle Quarry (Aggetts Ltd.) near Okehampton. Sandstone is quarried at Bishop's Court Quarry (English China Clays), near the M5 Granada motorway service station but the cementing there is weak, so this material is only used as sand for the building trade

An old medieval quarry can be seen on private ground at Exewell Barton farm, near Exminster, and sandstone cliffs near the motorway bridge at Exminster, with a similar exposure at the roundabout where the A379 turns towards Dawlish from the old Exeter by-pass.

TYPICAL BUILDINGS
Some red Permian sandstone blocks have been used inside Exeter Cathedral, in the north and south walls, and also in parts of house walls in Exmouth and Topsham. Devonian and Carboniferous sandstones can be seen in many older buildings in north Devon, including the parapet of Barnstaple Bridge. More recent are the public loos at Bessom Bridge, Wimbleball Lake.

3 BRECCIAS

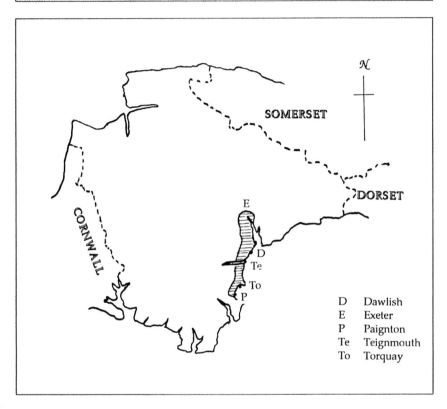

D   Dawlish
E   Exeter
P   Paignton
Te   Teignmouth
To   Torquay

Breccias are best regarded as sandstones, with a fraction of gravel fragments: they are cemented together with calcium carbonate, iron oxides or, perhaps, silica, just as are sandstones. However, the angular particles of the breccias are clearly visible without a hand lens, even to those with poor sight; in fact, some of the cemented stone fragments in the Tor Bay area are over 500 mm. long (see the exposure in the Newton Abbot direction, opposite Torre railway station, for instance).

The stone fragments can be of any type of rock but are mainly of limestone in the Tor Bay area, and of sandstone, quartz, quartzite, rhyolite, granite etc, elsewhere east and north east of Torquay. Within the breccias of the Dawlish to Exeter areas, including the Heavitree Stone, there are commonly fine grained sandstone infils, due, probably, to water borne sand migrating to fill spaces between the coarser gravel fragments.

The breccias are all red coloured, due to the presence of iron oxide, a common feature of the Permian rocks.

Quarries: The old Heavitree quarry, off Quarry Lane, Exeter, is virtually built over but some rock face is still visible. In the Dawlish to Paignton coastal cliffs the breccias can be examined at close hand. Being a stone of such variable durability, particularly when its bedding plane is ignored by the mason when used for building, it has fallen out of use. The Romans recognised its fallability when constructing their Exeter fort and shunned it in preference to the "trap" rock.

TYPICAL BUILDINGS
The numerous medieval churches in the centre of Exeter (except Mary Arches), Kenton church, and in Paignton, the Lloyds Bank, 2 Palace Avenue, and the Coverdale Tower.

4 GRANITE

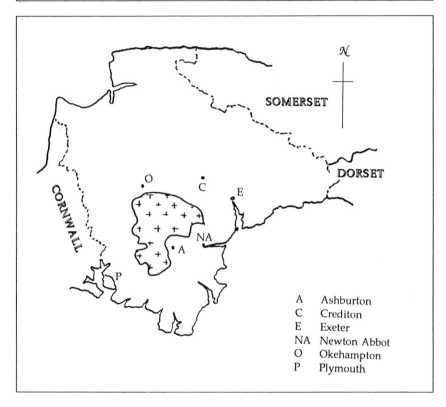

A   Ashburton
C   Crediton
E   Exeter
NA Newton Abbot
O   Okehampton
P   Plymouth

Granite is an igneous rock which cooled at depth in the Earth's crust. The slow cooling caused the main minerals of the granite to grow to easily visible sizes, and the typical Dartmoor granite displays large cream coloured crystals of feldspar. These are normally rectangular in shape, sometimes achieving lengths of 80mm or more, and hexagonal shapes are also common. The other minerals of granite are grey looking quartz crystals, and the very dark brown, flakey mica mineral, biotite. In many

The Guildhall, Plymouth, built with Devonian limestone

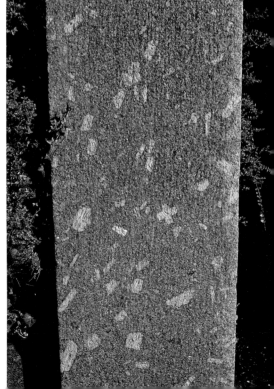

Dartmoor granite pillar in Denver Road, Topsham

Left: The medieval Gervase Bridge across the Exe in Exeter was largely built of trap

Below: Roman masons used both trap and Heavitree stone in this section of the wall round Exeter

Opposite above: Devonian slate hanging to be found off Plymouth Road, Tavistock

Opposite below: The Town Hall, Tavistock, has Hurdwick stone, Dartmoor granite and Devonian slate

Schist use as a walling stone in Salcombe

A cob wall in St. Leonard's Road, Exeter, with tiled head and Heavitree stone feet

Dartmoor granites there are also black looking aggregates of the mineral tourmaline – the pillars of the Exeter Guildhall front display these magnificently.

The overall appearance of Dartmoor granite is pale to medium grey, although, at times, brown iron staining can affect the colouration. It is a very durable building stone, and the crushing strength of Hay Tor granite, for instance, is over 6000 lbs per sq. in., so many of the structures in which granite has been used over the centuries are still standing.

The name 'granite' is from the sixteenth century Italian word 'granito' (grained), and came to be used in Britain about 1780. Before that the 'old men' knew it as moor stone; quarrying the stone is a comparatively recent activity. Old walls and buildings were constructed of stone from the moor's surface, often trimmed and dressed on the spot before removal.

Quarries: The only working quarry now left on Dartmoor is Merrivale Quarry, near Princetown (Tarmac) but many disused quarries can be seen scattered about the moor. Vast spoil heaps can be examined at Hay Tor, near Bovey Tracey, and also much of the track of the wagonway that took granite down off the moor to the Stover Canal; this wagonway is unique in Britain in that the track itself was cut from stone.

TYPICAL BUILDINGS
The Exeter Guildhall front pillars and pavement, most of the churches and farm buildings on Dartmoor, Princetown Prison and Castle Drogo, Drewsteignton. Kerbstones in cities and towns of the county, and boundary walls on and around Dartmoor.

5 TRAP (or BASALT)

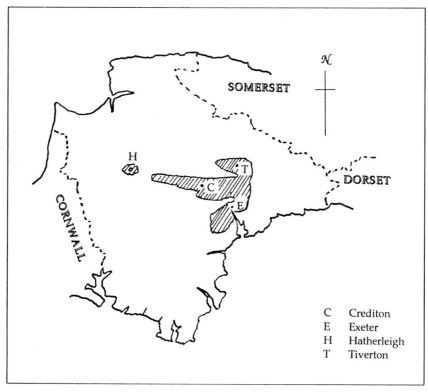

C	Crediton
E	Exeter
H	Hatherleigh
T	Tiverton

The trap (from the Scandinavian word 'trappe' – step) rocks are basalts which flowed out from volcanoes around Exeter – south as far as Dunchideock, north beyond Tiverton, east as far as Killerton, and west beyond Hatherleigh. These rocks are fine grained and a hand lens is necessary to see the minerals of the trap rocks. The trap which reached the Earth's surface, or very near it, is characterised by numerous holes, or vesicles, caused by the expansion of gases and steam within the molten rock before it cooled. In some instances these vesicles have become filled by minerals (usually calcium carbonate), brought in in solution, and the residual white mineral fillings visible in the rock, are called amygdales.

Some of the molten trap did not froth but, on cooling, cracked like shattered pottery, and the gaps were similarly filled with mineral veins, usually, again, of calcium carbonate. Very occasionally the trap neither frothed nor cracked, but still cooled rapidly, thus ensuring that the mineral crystals are small.

The trap rocks vary in colour from a pale grey to pink, red or purple. Care must be exercised that the trap is not confused with a fine grained sandstone – a hand lens to examine the crystal sizes and shapes should help.

Quarries: No working quarries exist, the last worked being the School Wood Quarry, near Dunchideock, and Pocombe Quarry (now a residential caravan site) at the top of Dunsford Hill, Exeter.

TYPICAL BUILDINGS
In Exeter, trap was used in Rougemont Castle, in much of the old Roman Wall and in the Royal Albert Memorial Museum. It can also be seen in many houses in Hatherleigh, in the chapel at Killerton and the parish church of Bradninch.

6 DOLERITE

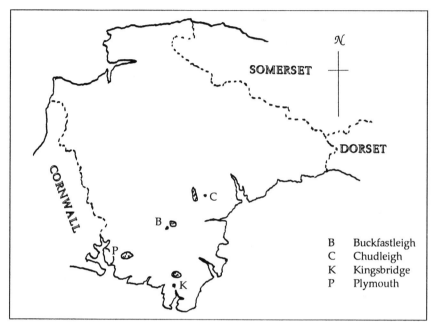

Dolerite (formerly known in Britain as diabase) is an igneous rock, similar to basalt. It is a fine grained, grey-green rock, and is very durable. It is known in the stone trade as Greenstone.

Quarries: Torr Quarry, near Kingsbridge, New England Quarry at Lee Mill 10 km east of Plymouth (English China Clays), and Whitecleaves Quarry, at Buckfastleigh (ARC) produce dolerite aggregates for the construction industry. Trusham Quarry in the Teign valley near Chudleigh (ARC) produces some dressed stone.

TYPICAL BUILDINGS: No buildings are known but dolerite was used, particulaly in Exeter, as kerbstones and can be seen near the Civic Building in Paris Street, for instance.

7 SLATE

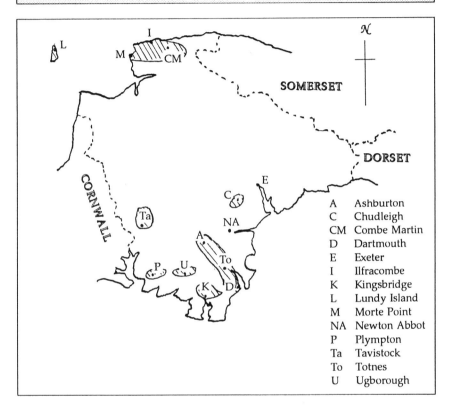

SOMERSET

DORSET

CORNWALL

A	Ashburton
C	Chudleigh
CM	Combe Martin
D	Dartmouth
E	Exeter
I	Ilfracombe
K	Kingsbridge
L	Lundy Island
M	Morte Point
NA	Newton Abbot
P	Plympton
Ta	Tavistock
To	Totnes
U	Ugborough

Slate is familiar to us all as a roofing material but there are some areas in Devon where local slate has been used as a building stone. Slate is what geologists call a metamorphic rock, that is it has been changed within the Earth's crust by heat and/or pressure. This change has caused the platey minerals (mainly micas) to grow in one plane, so that the resulting slate is similar in constitution to the leaves of a book which have been tightly stuck together. It is this structure of slate which makes it so useful for splitting into sheets (cleavage), as for roofing. It is the leaflike texture which readily identifies slate when used in buildings.

In Devon, stress during ancient mountain building episodes re-folded the slates and, particularly in south Devon, they have acquired cleavages in more than one direction. The slates of the South Hams, for instance, are liable to split into pyramid shapes. Nevertheless, many of the older buildings in the South Hams are of slate blocks which had obviously been carefully selected for shaping as building stone. These grey slates are not, generally speaking, high quality building materials, being softer than the slates of north Wales or the Lake District, for instance. As a consequence they are not likely to be found in buildings beyond easy transport distance of the old South Hams quarries.

Mill Hill slate, from the Tavistock area, is extensively used as a rockery stone, fireplace construction, and as a decorative stone on shop fronts. Its blue, green, grey and brown iron oxide colourings make it almost indistiguishable from the better known Delabole slate from Cornwall.

Still in the Tavistock area, there is another slate-like stone which was obtained there and used in building many structures in Tavistock, and churches in the vicinity. This is the Hurdwick stone, a metamophosed tuff (volcanic ash), very similar to the Westmoreland slates of the Lake District, and like them, it is of a light green colour. Within the stone there are frequent darker green blotches, and, just occasionally, pale buff, coarse grained, long oval-shaped inclusions.

The rusty brown faces of the Mill Hill slate can easily be mistaken for the similarly coloured north Devon sandstones. A scratch with a penknife blade will reveal which is which. The slate will be gouged by the metal, whereas the sandstone will abrade the knife blade.

Quarries: In the distant past slate was quarried for building purposes in several parts of Devon, although none were of high quality. These quarries were at Cann, near Tavistock, Gurrington, near Newton Abbot, Whiteway, near Chudleigh, and in north Devon at Morte Point, Lynmouth, Ilfracombe, Combe Martin, from Baggy Point to Croyde and on Lundy Island.

More recently, slate was quarried at Penn Recca, near Staverton, at Diptford, Ugborough, Plympton and at Woodland, near Ashburton. The South Hams slate was quarried at Kingsbridge, Frogmore, Charleton, Buckland Tout Saints, East Allington and Beesands. At present, slate is quarried at Chillaton Quarry (Marlow Stone [Chillaton] Ltd.) and Mill Hill and Longford Quarries (Mill Hill Quarry [Tavistock] Ltd.). just to the north of Tavistock. The Hurdwick stone, originally quarried by monks, is no longer worked, the old quarry being within the precincts of the Hurdwick Golf Club, on the Brentor road out of Tavistock.

TYPICAL BUILDINGS

Slate was used on most of the old houses and shops in the Kingsbridge area, and can be seen as cladding on old buildings in Ashburton, Buckfastleigh, Totnes, Tavistock and Dartmouth, and on 1 Catherine Street (currently the SPCK shop) and the Tudor House in Exeter.

Mill Hill slate has been used on the front of the White Hart Vaults, 64 South Street and the Blue Boy shop, 22 Princesshay, Exeter.

Hurdwick stone was used in many of the old buildings in Tavistock, including the Town Hall and the Bedford Hotel.

8 SCHIST

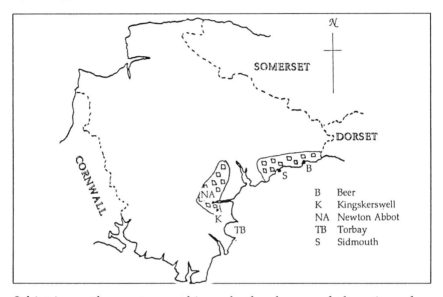

Schist is another metamorphic rock, the degree of alteration of the structure of the stone having undergone more change than slate, particularly regarding its minerals, which have become extensively altered. It is generally of a blue-green or beige colour, with wavey or curling textures, crumbling fairly readily after long exposure on the external walls of a building. It is unlikely to be found as a building material outside the Salcombe-Start Point area as it was scarcely worth transporting further.

Quarries: None now exist,and it was probably taken from small locally available sites which have now been used as building sites or for infilling.

TYPICAL BUILDINGS: Many of the older buildings and walls in the Salcombe area are built of this stone.

9 'BUDLEIGH BUNS'

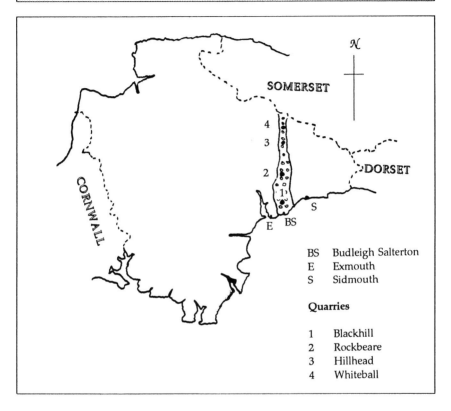

BS   Budleigh Salterton
E   Exmouth
S   Sidmouth

Quarries

1   Blackhill
2   Rockbeare
3   Hillhead
4   Whiteball

Budleigh Buns are so named because their shape is similar to baked buns, or baps. They are water rounded cobbles of quartzite, a form of sandstone of sedimentary origin, now highly metamorphosed. They are normally pale grey in colour, but some have pinkish tinges or patches. They have not been used to any great extent as building stone – their shape and hardness preclude this – but they have been used as wall facings in a decorative style. These days, the buns are used in areas where, for various reasons, someone has decided that pedestrians should not walk; they are uncomfortable to the feet when suitably spaced.

Quarries: The buns were formerly removed from the beach at Budleigh Salterton but now that that activity is not permitted, the cobbles are produced by sieving weathered conglomerate at workings along a north-south line from Bampton to Budleigh Salterton, on the outcrop of the Budleigh Salterton Pebble Beds. These workings are at Blackhill Quarry near Exmouth (English China Clays), and Venn Ottery, Hill Head near Uffculme and White Ball near Wellington, all belonging to English China Clays.

TYPICAL BUILDINGS
Many old buildings in south-east Devon, between Exmouth and Sidmouth.

10 FLINT

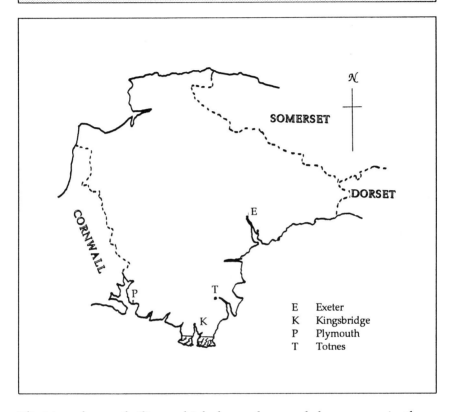

SOMERSET

DORSET

CORNWALL

N

E

T

P

K

E	Exeter
K	Kingsbridge
P	Plymouth
T	Totnes

Flint is a form of silica, which formed as nodular masses in the chalk, a soft limestone, which once overlaid the whole of south and east Devon. Flint can be black, grey or white, and is used mainly as a decorative stone to face walls of buildings in a similar way to the Budleigh Buns. When used for this purpose it is usually napped: the glassy interior is revealed by knocking the stone with a hammer or another piece of flint.

Quarries: There are no working quarries as such, although the Royal Aller Vale Quarry near Kingskerswell (ARC), and Haldon Quarry between Exeter and Newton Abbot (Haldon Quarries Ltd), work flint gravels. In the past flint was removed from south-east Devon beaches, or from local small quarries which were short-lived.

TYPICAL BUILDINGS
St. Paul's Church, Chudleigh Knighton; Allhallows School (between Axmouth and Lyme Regis); and numerous buildings in Beer and south-east Devon.

11 COB

Whilst not a building stone as such, cob walls were used in buildings in many parts of Devon. Cob is essentially a mixture of clay with various binding materials, such as straw, horsehair, sheep's wool, gravel, cow manure and almost anything which was to hand. It was usual to heap the materials in a byre, where they were mixed by the animals' feet – natural manure input resulted! The wall was built slowly, preferably between shuttering, and the mixture of materials was brought to a dough-like consistency, using water. The cob wall had to be constructed on a pervious stone base, and its apex capped with roofing of some sort, such as tiles or thatch. This ensured that the wall's 'head and feet' were kept dry. In many cases the cob wall was rendered with cement or a lime wash to help keep it dry but this coating could be self defeating, by retaining water seeping in through flaws in the capping. A sudden and dramatic collapse of the wall can thus easily occur, particularly during heavy rain or in frosty conditions. Although it may look rather vulnerable to the weather, a cob wall lasts well if it is left naked to the elements. It dries out quite rapidly.

A cob wall is usually easily identified by its muddy, gritty appearance, and, because of its method of construcion, does not consist of blocks cemented together, unlike a mason-built stone wall.

Quarries: All the materials were virtually to hand, so no quarrying was necessary.

TYPICAL BUILDINGS: Many old barns, outbuildings and boundary walls throughout Devon. Examples can be seen in St. Leonard's Road, Exeter (near the Royal School for the Deaf), and on the A379, near Peamore House.

SHORT NOTE ON SOME TERMS USED IN THIS GUIDE

Sedimentary rocks are derived from the consolidation of particles of rock debris which have settled in water, air or ice. The particles are normally cemented together with minerals such as silica (SiO_2) or calcite ($CaCO_3$). Typical examples are sandstones and limestones.

Igneous rocks are those which have solidified from molten rock material (magma) and have come from deep in the Earth's crust or mantle. Typical examples are granite and basalt.

Metamorphic rocks are rocks of any type, which have been altered by heat and/or pressure within the Earth's crust. The alteration is a partial or complete re-crystallization of the original rock, to form the new stone, which may include newly formed minerals. Typical examples are slate and marble.

GEOLOGICAL TIMETABLE OF DEVON'S ROCKS

Period	Span in millions of years ago
Quaternary	Present - 1.64
Tertiary	1.64 - 65
Cretaceous	65 - 146
Jurassic	146 - 208
Triassic	208 - 245
Permian	245 - 290
Carboniferous	290 - 363
Devonian	363 - 409

BIBLIOGRAPHY

The Geology of Devon, edited by E. M. Durrance & D. J. C. Laming, University of Exeter (1982), ISBN 0 85989 153 4.

Geology Explained in South and East Devon, J. W. Perkins, David & Charles (1971), 0 7153 5304 7.

Geology Explained, Dartmoor and the Tamar Valley, J. W. Perkins, David & Charles (1972), 0 7153 5516 3.

Geology of Construction Materials, J. E. Prentice, Chapman & Hall (1990), 0 412 29740 X.

Dictionary of Geology, D. F. Lapidus & I. Winstanley, Collins (1990), 0 00434 148 1.

The Physical Geography of Landscape, R. Collard, Collins (1991), 0 00322 285 3.

Devon's Traditional Buildings, Devon County Council (1978), 0 86114 059 1.

The Devonshire Association was formed in 1862 to encourage the study of science, literature and the arts within the county. The Association began publishing the results of such study from the start, producing its first *Transactions* in 1862. *Transactions* have continued in an unbroken series ever since and regularly contain a wide variety of papers that are themselves the basis of research around the world. The Association also publishes other work which throws new light on the county, as much about its present as its past.

Further information about these publications, about the lectures, visits and study weeks arranged by the Association and about personal or corporate membership are available from:
The Registrar, The Devonshire Association, 7 Cathedral Close, Exeter EX1 1EZ, England.